MIND BENDERS® A2

DEDUCTIVE THINKING SKILLS

SERIES TITLES

Mind Benders® Warm Up, Mind Benders® A1, Mind Benders® A2, Mind Benders® A3, Mind Benders® A4, Mind Benders® B1, Mind Benders® B2, Mind Benders® B3, Mind Benders® B4, Mind Benders® C1, Mind Benders® C2, Mind Benders® C3

DATE DUE

ANITA HARNADEK

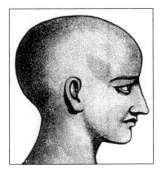

© 2000, 1978
THE CRITICAL THINKING COMPANY
www.CriticalThinking.com
P.O. Box 448 • Pacific Grove • CA 93950-0448
Phone 800-458-4849 • FAX 831-393-3277
ISBN 0-89455-018-7
Printed in the United States of America

TABLE OF CONTENTS

INTRODUCTORY INFORMATION

EXERCISES

SOLUTIONS

EXAMPLES AND STEP-BY-STEP PROCEDURES

TEACHER SUGGESTIONS

PURPOSE

Students having wide ranges of ability, motivation, and achievement seem to be remarkably attracted to Mind Benders® problems. Students who may or may not try to use deductive reasoning for ordinary classwork or homework seem to think Mind Benders® are fun, not work. So the purpose of the MIND BENDERS® series is to give each student what (s)he wants—fun, a happy diversion from routine—while at the same time forcing the student to organize sets of clues—some direct, some indirect—and reach logical conclusions by using pure deductive reasoning.

GENERAL INFORMATION

There are twelve exercise books in this series:

WARM-UP MIND BENDERS®

MIND BENDERS® A1

MIND BENDERS® A2

MIND BENDERS® A3

MIND BENDERS® A4

MIND BENDERS® B1

MIND BENDERS® B2

MIND BENDERS® B3

MIND BENDERS® B4

MIND BENDERS® C1

MIND BENDERS® C2

MIND BENDERS® C3

The **A** series is easy, **B** is medium, and **C** is hard.

Although most of the problems in WARM UP MIND BENDERS® vary from extremely easy to easy, there are a handful in the medium range. The idea of the problems in the warmup book is to give the students practice in using deductive reasoning in very simple situations before presenting them with more clues to use and with clues which are more subtle, as in the other MIND BENDERS® books.

Since some teachers will need more problems for their students than other teachers, more than one book is available in each of the A, B, and C categories. Within a category, there is no substantial difference in difficulty between the books offered. (For example, a teacher who needs only 15 problems at the easy level may order any of the four MIND BENDERS® books in the A series.)

See page iv for general comments about assumptions that can be made from clues.

HELPFUL HINTS ABOUT SOLVING MIND BENDERS®

Most Mind Benders® in the A, B, and C categories are solved more easily if a chart is used than if the solver simply makes notes about the clues given. To help students solve the problems, each Mind Bender® is accompanied by a chart made especially for that particular problem.

See page vi for a step-by-step explanation of using charts to solve Mind Bender® problems, including the way each chart looks after each step. None of the problems used there are used as exercises in any of the MIND BENDERS® books.

The instructions (in highly abbreviated form, of course) are these: To fill in a chart, make a notation in each square which is eliminated by a clue. (The notation might be the clue number or the word "no," for example.) When there is only one blank square left in a row (or column) within a category, then "X" that square. Then note the elimination of all the other squares in the matching column (or row). When a chart contains three or more categories, then either the elimination of a square or the "X"ing of a square may also give you more information about previous clues. (For example, if you know that Mr. Brown owns the red car and you have just discovered that the Chevrolet is not the red car, then you have also discovered that Mr. Brown does not own the Chevrolet.)

SOLUTIONS

Note 1: Each problem has only one solution. If the notation used for eliminations is simply a "no," then the completed chart will have an "X" for each combination named in the solutions given below, and the chart will have a "no" everywhere else. If the notation used for elimination is a clue number, however, then the completed chart may vary from one student to another. (This is because eliminations can sometimes be made in different orders.)

Note 2: If your solutions do not agree with those given, refer to How to Use a Chart on page vi for or the Examples and Step-by-Step Procedures on page 33 for information on how to use charts to solve Mind Benders® problems.

About the Clues in MIND BENDERS®

In general, the MIND BENDERS® assume that you will, when using the clues, apply three guidelines unless a problem leads you to believe otherwise:

1. Think of everyday situations rather than of highly unusual exceptions.

2. Think of standards which are generally acceptable to U.S. society as a whole.

3. Use common sense and context in deciding what the clues mean.

Following are examples:

a. Assume that only males have male names (John, Robert, Dave) and only females have female names (Mary, Jennifer, Cathy). But be careful not to make such assumptions about unisex names (Pat, Chris).

b. Assume that typical U.S. social relationships apply. For example, if John is engaged to Mary, you may assume they know each other. You may assume that very close relatives know each other.

c. Don't assume that rare age relationships may apply. For example, don't assume that a 7 year old might be a college graduate, or that a parent might be younger than his or her adopted child. On the other hand, although most cases of age may be in one direction, enough cases in the other direction may exist so that these would not be considered especially unusual. For example, a husband may be a good deal younger than his wife, or a 45 year old may get the mumps.

d. Assume that animals are of normal size. For example, "a horse" is not "a pygmy horse"; "a small dog" is smaller than a goat; a "large dog" is simply one of the larger breeds of dogs. If a problem talks about a cat and a fox, assume that the cat is smaller than the fox. Do not think that maybe the cat is fully grown and the fox is a few weeks old.

e. Assume that animals are called by their usual names within the context. For example, if John and Mary have a pet dog and a pet cat, assume that the cat is an ordinary household cat, rather than maybe a tiger or a leopard.

f. Don't look for tricky situations. For example, suppose the problem has four houses in a row (and no other houses). And suppose Debby lives next door to Gary. Don't assume that Debby or Gary might live in a garage between two of the houses. That is, assume that they live in two of the four houses in the problem.

g. Assume that typical U.S. social situations apply. For example, if John went on a date with Abbott, assume two things: (1) Abbott is a female; (2) neither John nor Abbott is married, since (a) when a married couple go out, we do not call it a "date," and (b) if either one is married to someone else, then it is not typical for him or her to be dating someone.

h. Pay attention to what the clues say. For example, suppose a problem has four people, and suppose one clue says, "Cathy and the dentist ride to work together in a car pool." Also suppose another clue says, "Brown, who does not know any of the other three people, is not the typist." Then you should deduce that neither Cathy nor the dentist is Brown.

i. Exact wording to eliminate ambiguities sometimes makes a clue too long. The clue is then shortened to the point where it is unambiguous to most people, but some people would still recognize ambiguities and object to the wording. In such cases, consider the context and the intent of the clue. As examples:

(1) "Neither Bob nor Young lives in the white house," means, "Bob is not Young, and Bob does not live in the white house, and Young does not live in the white house."

(2) "John and Abbott went bowling with Dave and Smith," means, "Four different people went bowling together. One of these was John, one was Abbott, one was Dave, and one was Smith."

(3) "Jane doesn't know either Mary or the artist," means, "Jane doesn't know Mary, and Jane doesn't know the artist, and Mary is not the artist."

(4) "Neither Carol nor Bill went to the party, and Norris didn't go, either," refers to three different people.

(5) In general, "neither ... nor" and "either ... or" sentences will refer to separate things, as in the above examples. Just plain "or" sentences, however, are sometimes less definite, as in this example: "Neither Becky nor Jackson has the dog or is the secretary." Here, Becky and Jackson are different people, but we aren't sure that the person who has the dog is not also the secretary.

MISCELLANEOUS INFORMATION

Most of the problems you will find that are similar to these Mind Benders® seem to be good ones, but you may run into some that could be better. Here are examples of clues from such problems:

1. One clue reads, "Abbott told Baker that he could beat her at weight lifting." You can't tell which one is the man and which is the woman from this sentence. It may be that a man (Abbott) is claiming that he can beat a woman (Baker) at weight lifting, or it may be that a woman (Abbott) is claiming that a man (Baker) can beat her at weight lifting.

2. One clue tells you that Abbott is single, and another clue refers to John's children. You don't know whether or not the writer thinks that single people don't have children. (Maybe he adopted children.)

3. Some problems have contradictory clues. I once saw a problem in which one clue said that Abbott spent all of his spare time doing one thing (reading, for example), and another clue said that John was doing something else with his friends (watching TV, for example). So I marked on the chart that John was not Abbott. But a few minutes later I found the problem to be unsolvable, so I looked at the solution which came with it. The solution showed that John was Abbott.

HOW TO USE A CHART

A Mind Bender® problem gives you two or more lists of things and asks you to match each item in one list with an item in the other list. Finding answers is easier if a chart is made showing all the lists at once and is then filled in. For more detailed examples, see page 33.

Note that the number of small boxes (within a large box) is the square of the number of things in any one list (Example 1 has three things in each list, so each large box has 9 small boxes).

EXAMPLE of a TWO-DIMENSIONAL PROBLEM

Davis, Edwards, and Jones are an astronaut, a computer programmer, and a skin diver.

1. Davis is not the astronaut or the computer programmer.

2. Jones is not the astronaut.

What does each person do?

Solution:

Make a chart and use clue 1—put "no" in D/A and D/CP. This leaves only one blank space in the "D" row. Write X to show that Davis is the skin diver.

Since we know that Davis is the skin diver, we can fill in the other spaces in the "SD" column. Write "no" for both Edwards and Jones.

We are through with the first clue, so now we can use the second clue. Write "no" in J/A to show Jones is not the astronaut.

The "A" column now has only one blank space, so we X it to show that Edwards is the astronaut. (The "J" row also has only one blank space, but it is a good idea to work on only one row or column at a time.)

The "E" row has only one remaining blank space, so we write "no" (since Edwards is the astronaut, he is not the computer programmer).

In the "J" row, one space remains, so we X it (Jones is the programmer).

The chart now shows the solution: Davis is the skin diver, Edwards is the astronaut, and Jones is the computer programmer.

	A	CP	SD
D	no	no	X
E			
J			

	A	CP	SD
D	no	no	X
E			no
J			no

	A	CP	SD
D	no	no	X
E			no
J	no		no

	A	CP	SD
D	no	no	X
E	X		no
J	no		no

	A	CP	SD
D	no	no	X
E	X	no	no
J	no		no

	A	CP	SD
D	no	no	X
E	X	no	no
J	no	X	no

1. Order of Age

Melissa is younger than Natalie and is older and shorter than Jason. Natalie is taller and younger than Ken, but Ken is taller than Jason.

List the ages of the four people in order, starting with the oldest.

List the heights of the four people in order, starting with the tallest.

2. Favorite Colors

The favorite colors of Betty, Carol, Dick, and Joe are green, pink, red, and yellow.

1. No person's name has the same number of letters as his or her favorite color.

2. Carol and the girl who likes pink are in different grades.

3. Red is the favorite color of one of the boys.

Find each person's favorite color.

Chart for Problem 2

	green	pink	red	yellow
Betty				
Carol				
Dick				
Joe				

3. What's for Breakfast?

Gerry, Holly and Joe each ate something different for breakfast. One had cereal, one had eggs, and one had French toast.

1. Joe did not have eggs or French toast.

2. Holly did not have eggs.

What did each person eat?

Chart for Problem 3

	cereal	eggs	French toast
Gerry			
Holly			
Joe			

4.   A Tougher Problem

Ichabod, Lloyd, and Otto live in Illinois, Louisiana, and Oregon. One drinks iced water, one drinks lemonade, and one drinks orange juice.

1. Nobody lives in a state or drinks something which starts with the same letter as his name starts with.

2. The state where each person lives starts with a letter that is different from the first letter of his drink.

3. Ichabod does not live in Louisiana.

Where does each person live?

What does each person drink?

Chart for Problem 4

	Illinois	Louisiana	Oregon	iced water	lemonade	orange juice
Ichabod						
Lloyd						
Otto						
iced water			
lemonade			
orange juice			

5.   How They Earn Their Money

Angelo, Becky, Conrad, and Doreen are an actor, a bellhop, a comedian, and a trapeze artist. From the clues below, match each person's name and occupation.

1. Doreen is not in show business.

2. Neither Becky nor Angelo is the actor.

3. People never laugh when Becky is working.

Chart for Problem 5

	actor	bellhop	comedian	trapeze artist
Angelo				
Becky				
Conrad				
Doreen				

6. Three Daughters

Alice, Brenda, and Celeste are the daughters of Dwight, Edna, and Frank, who are a butcher, a carpenter, and a doctor. Use the clues below to match up everything.

1. The carpenter's daughter's best friend is Alice, but she's very fond of Brenda, too.

2. Dwight's daughter invited Brenda and the doctor's daughter to a party.

3. Edna is not the doctor.

Chart for Problem 6

	butcher	carpenter	doctor	Alice	Brenda	Celeste
Dwight						
Edna						
Frank						
Alice						
Brenda						
Celeste						

7. Height Classification

Five people (Uriah, Vivian, Wagner, Yvonne, and Zennia) were all different heights. From the information which follows, list their names in the order of their heights, starting with the shortest.

1. Wagner was taller than Uriah and shorter than Vivian.

2. Yvonne was taller than Vivian.

3. Zennia was taller than Uriah and shorter than Wagner.

Chart for Problem 7

	1 shortest	2	3	4	5 tallest
Uriah					
Vivian					
Wagner					
Yvonne					
Zennia					

8.   A Construction Tale

Cornelius, Dolly, and Lorna each used something different to try to stick two sheets of paper together. One used glue, one used paste, and one used rubber cement. Their last names are Kingman, Marner, and Norwood.

1. Norwood and the girl who used paste did neat jobs.

2. Marner likes to play catch with his father.

3. Dolly's name is not Kingman.

4. Cornelius did not use glue.

What is each person's full name, and what did (s)he use?

Chart for Problem 8

	Kingman	Marner	Norwood	glue	paste	rubber cement
Cornelius						
Dolly						
Lorna						
glue			
paste			
rubber cement			

9.   Names and Ages

The last names of two girls (Leota and Orchid) and two boys (Min-Tan and Patrick) are Berry, Richards, Salton, and Young. The ages are 8, 10, 11, and 12.

Find each person's full name and age.

1. Salton told his father that Young said she was going to beat him up.

2. Min-Tan and the 8-year-old boy have the same music teacher.

3. Berry is older than Orchid and younger than Leota.

4. Richards is the oldest.

Chart for Problem 9

	Berry	Richards	Salton	Young	8	10	11	12
Leota								
Min-Tan								
Orchid								
Patrick								
8								
10								
11								
12								

10. Cars and Colors

The cars of Arnett, Bradley, Church, and Dawson are gray, red, silver, and yellow.

Find each person's name and car color.

1. Bradley and Church had lunch yesterday with the owner of the silver car.

2. Dawson saw the owners of the red car and the gray car passing his house yesterday.

3. The owner of the yellow car thinks he got a better deal on his car than Arnett and Dawson got on theirs.

4. Bradley's car is not a bright color.

Chart for Problem 10

	gray	red	silver	yellow
Arnett				
Bradley				
Church				
Dawson				

11. A Glimpse of Royalty

Claudia, Eunice, Ferdinand, and Horace are a king, a queen, a prince, and a princess. Claudia and the princess beat Ferdinand and the king at playing Monopoly.

What is each person's rank?

Chart for Problem 11

	king	prince	princess	queen
Claudia				
Eunice				
Ferdinand				
Horace				

12. Progressive Pattern

George wrote the letters A, B, C, and D in a certain order.

1. He wrote C before B and after D.

2. He wrote A after D and before C.

In what order did George write the letters?

Chart for Problem 12

	1st	2nd	3rd	4th
A				
B				
C				
D				

13. Transportation Schedule

Riley, Shulte, and White all went to Los Angeles. One took a bus, one took a plane, and one took a train. Find out how each person went.

1. Riley and the person who went on the plane live next door to each other.

2. White and the person who rode the bus left at different times.

3. Riley did not go on the bus.

Chart for Problem 13

	bus	plane	train
Riley			
Shulte			
White			

14. The School Play

Anna, Luis, Ramon, and Thomas have parts in the school play. Their roles are a butler, a detective, a model, and a songwriter.

Find each person's role in the play.

1. Someone told the detective that she wasn't learning her lines fast enough.

2. Everyone likes the way Luis and the butler are acting their roles.

3. Thomas, Luis, and the model live on the same street.

Chart for Problem 14

	butler	detective	model	songwriter
Anna				
Luis				
Ramon				
Thomas				

15. The Big Test

Dori, Juanita, and Leona each had a test today. One test was in music, one was in reading, and one was in spelling. The test grades were A, B, and C.

1. Dori's grade was lower than both Juanita's grade and the reading test grade.

2. The spelling test grade was higher than the reading test grade.

What test did each person take, and what was the grade on the test?

Chart for Problem 15

	music	reading	spelling	A	B	C
Dori						
Juanita						
Leona						
A			
B			
C			

SOLUTIONS

GENERAL COMMENTS ABOUT SOLUTIONS

There is more than one way to approach the solution of most Mind Benders®. For example, if a problem has five clues, you might choose to apply clue 4 first and clue 2 second, while the solution here for that problem uses clue 3 first and clue 5 second. Since there is only one final answer to the problem, the order in which the clues are used does not affect the final answer.

In order to understand a solution here, it is necessary that you have a copy of the problem to refer to while you are reading the solution. Also, it is definitely suggested, particularly for the problems in the B and C series, that you write down the findings as you go through a solution in order to help keep track of the rationale. For example, suppose a problem uses first and last names and occupations of three people. Before you start reading the solution here, write down the first names, leaving space to fill in the last names and occupations:

> Bernard
>
> Catherine
>
> Donald

Then this is what your notes will look like as you read through (part of) the detailed solution, "Smith is a man (2) but isn't Donald (4), so he is Bernard."

> Bernard Smith
>
> Catherine
>
> Donald

"The TV repairer is a man (3) but isn't Smith (3), so he is Donald."

> Bernard Smith
>
> Catherine
>
> Donald,　　　　TV repairer

Notice in the above example that clue numbers are referred to in parentheses.

DETAILED SOLUTIONS

1.

AGES (oldest first)	HEIGHTS (tallest first)
Ken	Natalie
Natalie	Ken
Melissa	Jason
Jason	Melissa

For ages, we have (first sentence) Natalie, Melissa, Jason, and (second sentence) Ken, Natalie. For heights, we have (first sentence) Jason, Melissa, and (second sentence) Natalie, Ken, and Jason. Combining these, we have the solution shown.

2.

NAME	COLOR
Betty	pink
Carol	yellow
Dick	red
Joe	green

Red is a boy's favorite color (3) but not Joe's (1), so it is Dick's. Green is not the favorite color of Betty or Carol (1), so it is Joe's. Pink isn't Carol's favorite (2), so it is Betty's, and Carol's favorite is yellow.

3.

NAME	FOOD
Gerry	eggs
Holly	French toast
Joe	cereal

Joe had cereal (1). Holly didn't have eggs (2), so she had French toast. Then Gerry had eggs.

4.

NAME	STATE	DRINK
Ichabod	Oregon	lemonade
Lloyd	Illinois	orange juice
Otto	Louisiana	iced water

Ichabod doesn't live in Illinois (1) or Louisiana (3), so he lives in Oregon. He doesn't drink iced water (1) or orange juice (2), so he drinks lemonade. Lloyd doesn't live in Louisiana (1), so he lives in Illinois. He doesn't drink iced water (2), so he drinks orange juice. Then Otto lives in Louisiana and drinks iced water.

5.

NAME	JOB
Angelo	comedian
Becky	trapeze artist
Conrad	actor
Doreen	bellhop

Doreen is the bellhop (1). Then Conrad is the actor (2). Becky is not the comedian (3), so Angelo is, and Becky is the trapeze artist.

6.

PARENT	JOB	DAUGHTER
Dwight	carpenter	Celeste
Edna	butcher	Brenda
Frank	doctor	Alice

The doctor is not Dwight (2) or Edna (3), so Frank is the doctor. Brenda is not the carpenter's daughter (1) or the doctor's daughter (2), so she is the butcher's daughter. She isn't Dwight's daughter (2), so Dwight isn't the butcher. Then Edna is the butcher, and Dwight is the carpenter. Dwight's daughter isn't Alice (1), so she is Celeste. Then Frank's daughter is Alice.

7.

SHORTEST				TALLEST
Uriah	Zennia	Wagner	Vivian	Yvonne

From clue 1, we have U<W<V. Using clue 2 with this, we get U<W<V<Y. Clue 3 puts Zennia between Uriah and Wagner, so we have U<Z<W<V<Y.

8.

FIRST NAME	LAST NAME	ADHESIVE
Cornelius	Marner	rubber cement
Dolly	Norwood	glue
Lorna	Kingman	paste

Marner is a boy (2), so he is Cornelius. He did not use glue (4) or paste (1, girl), so he used rubber cement. Dolly isn't Kingman (3), so Lorna is, and so Dolly is Norwood. Norwood didn't use paste (1), so Kingman did, and so Norwood used glue.

9.

FIRST NAME	LAST NAME	AGE
Leota	Richards	12
Min-Tan	Berry	11
Orchid	Young	10
Patrick	Salton	8

The 8 year old is a boy (2) but isn't Min-Tan, so he is Patrick. Orchid isn't 11 or 12 (3), so she is 10. Then Berry is 11 and Leota is 12 (3). This means Min-Tan is Berry. Also, Leota is Richards (4). Salton is a boy (1), so he is Patrick, and Young is Orchid.

10.

NAME	CAR COLOR
Arnett	red
Bradley	gray
Church	yellow
Dawson	silver

The yellow car isn't owned by Arnett or Dawson (3) or Bradley (4), so Church owns it. Dawson's car isn't gray or red (2), so it is silver. Bradley's car isn't red (4), so it is gray, and so Arnett's car is red.

11.

NAME	RANK
Claudia	queen
Eunice	princess
Ferdinand	prince
Horace	king

The king and the prince are males, while the queen and the princess are females. Claudia isn't the princess, so she is the queen, and so Eunice is the princess. Ferdinand isn't the king, so Horace is, and so Ferdinand is the prince.

12.

FIRST			LAST
D	A	C	B

From clue 1, we have D, C, B. From clue 2, we have D, A, C. Combining these, we have D, A, C, B.

13.

NAME	TRANS-PORTATION
Riley	train
Shulte	bus
White	plane

Riley didn't go by plane (1) or by bus (3), so he went by train. White didn't go by bus (2), so Shulte did, and so White went by plane.

14.

NAME	ROLE
Anna	detective
Luis	songwriter
Ramon	model
Thomas	butler

Anna is the only girl, so she is the detective (1). The model isn't Luis or Thomas (3), so he is Ramon. Luis isn't the butler (2), so Thomas is, and so Luis is the songwriter.

15.

NAME	TEST	GRADE
Dori	music	C
Juanita	spelling	A
Leona	reading	B

Neither Dori nor Juanita took the reading test (1), so Leona took it. Dori's grade was C (1). Then Dori didn't take the spelling test (2), so Juanita did, and so Dori took the music test. The reading test grade wasn't A (2), so the spelling test grade was A, and the reading test grade was B.

MORE EXAMPLES & STEP-BY-STEP PROCEDURES
(see page vi)

TWO-DIMENSIONAL PROBLEMS

EXAMPLE 1

Problem: Davis, Edwards, Farman, and Jones are an astronaut, a bookbinder, a computer programmer, and a skin diver. Find each person's job.

1. Neither Edwards nor Jones knows anything about computers.

2. Neither Davis nor Edwards can swim.

Solution:

1. Make the chart and use *clue 1*. (Astronauts have to know something about computers, and so do computer programmers. So Edwards is not the astronaut or the computer programmer, and neither is Jones.)

	A	B	CP	SD
D				
E	1		1	
F				
J	1		1	

2. There is more than one blank space left in each column and row, so we can't do anything more from *clue 1*. So we use *clue 2*. (Astronauts and skin divers have to know how to swim, so Davis is not the astronaut or the skin diver, and neither is Edwards.)

	A	B	CP	SD
D	2			2
E	1		1	2
F				
J	1		1	

3. There is only one space left in the "E" row, so we X it in.

	A	B	CP	SD
D	2			2
E	1	X	1	2
F				
J	1		1	

4. The "B" column is matched up now, so we fill in the rest of the blank spaces here.

	A	B	CP	SD
D	2	B		2
E	1	X	1	2
F		B		
J	1	B	1	

5. Now we X the only blank space in the "D" row.

	A	B	CP	SD
D	2	B	X	2
E	1	X	1	2
F		B		
J	1	B	1	

6. The "CP" column is matched now, so fill in the remaining blank.

	A	B	CP	SD
D	2	B	X	2
E	1	X	1	2
F		B	CP	
J	1	B	1	

7. The "J" row isn't matched yet, and there is only one blank left. So we X this blank.

	A	B	CP	SD
D	2	B	X	2
E	1	X	1	2
F		B	CP	
J	1	B	1	X

8. Now the "SD" column is matched, so we fill in the blank there.

	A	B	CP	SD
D	2	B	X	2
E	1	X	1	2
F		B	CP	SD
J	1	B	1	X

9. Finally, the only blank left is in the "F" row and "A" column. Neither the row nor the column is matched yet, so we X this blank.

We now have the solution: Davis, computer programmer; Edwards, bookbinder; Farman, astronaut; Jones, skin diver.

	A	B	CP	SD
D	2	B	X	2
E	1	X	1	2
F	X	B	CP	SD
J	1	B	1	X

Sometimes the clues are not so obvious.

EXAMPLE 2

Problem: Davis, Edwards, Farman, and Jones are an astronaut, a bookbinder, a computer programmer, and a skin diver. Find each person's job and sex.

1. Davis and her husband invited the bookbinder and his wife to dinner.

2. The computer programmer said he enjoys playing chess with Farman.

3. The skin diver congratulated Jones on her bowling score of 230 last night.

Solution:

If we simply make a chart and fill it in from the obvious clues, we have: *clue 1*, Davis is not the bookbinder; *clue 2*, Farman is not the computer programmer; *clue 3*, Jones is not the skin diver. So our chart looks like the one at the right, and we may think that the problem does not give enough information for a solution.

	A	B	CP	SD
D		1		
E				
F			2	
J				3

But wait. *Clue 1* says "Davis and **her** husband," so Davis is a female. (Mark "F" for "female" in the margin.) And *Clue 1* says "bookbinder and **his** wife," so the bookbinder is a male. (Mark "M" for "male" in the margin.)

M_1

	A	B	CP	SD
F_1 D		1		
E				
F				
J				

In *clue 2*, "he" is the computer programmer. And we already know that *clue 2* says Farman is not the computer programmer.

M_1 M_2

	A	B	CP	SD
F_1 D		1		
E				
F			2	
J				

Now the margins show Davis is a female and the computer programmer is a male, so Davis is not the computer programmer. We mark "FM" for "female-male" in the D/CP blank.

M_1 M_2

	A	B	CP	SD
F_1 D		1	FM	
E				
F			2	
J				

Now we are ready for *clue 3*. Here, "her" refers to Jones, so Jones is a female. We mark the margin. And we already know that *clue 3* says Jones is not the skin diver.

M_1 M_2

	A	B	CP	SD
F_1 D		1	FM	
E				
F			2	
F_3 J				3

Now Jones is a female, but the bookbinder and the computer programmer are males, so we fill in the blanks for J/B and for J/CP.

M_1 M_2

	A	B	CP	SD
F_1 D		1	FM	
E				
F			2	
F_3 J		FM	FM	3

There is only one blank left in the "CP" column, so we X it. It falls in the "E" row, so we also fill in the rest of the "E" row.

M_1 M_2

	A	B	CP	SD
F_1 D		1	FM	
E	E	E	X	E
F			2	
F_3 J		FM	FM	3

Now there is only one blank left in the "B" column, so we X it. It falls in the "F" row, so we also fill in the rest of this row.

		M₁	M₂		
		A	B	CP	SD
F₁	D		1	FM	
	E	E	E	X	E
	F	F	X	2	F
F₃	J		FM	FM	3

This leaves only one blank in the "SD" column, so we X this blank. Since this X is in the "D" row, we fill in the rest of the row, too.

		M₁	M₂		
		A	B	CP	SD
F₁	D	D	1	FM	X
	E	E	E	X	E
	F	F	X	2	F
F₃	J		FM	FM	3

We now have only one blank left, so we X it.

So the solution to the problem is this: Davis, skin diver, female; Edwards, computer programmer, male; Farman, bookbinder, male; Jones, astronaut, female.

		M₁	M₂		
		A	B	CP	SD
F₁	D	D	1	FM	X
	E	E	E	X	E
	F	F	X	2	F
F₃	J	X	FM	FM	3

EXAMPLE 3

Problem: Davis, Edwards, Farman, and Jones are an astronaut, a bookbinder, a computer programmer, and a skin diver. Find each person's job and sex.

1. Edwards is the bookbinder's son. (See note below.)

2. Jones's husband played golf with the computer programmer's husband.

3. The astronaut said Farman told her that he's going to Hawaii next month.

Note for *clue 1*: Since a son usually has the same last name as his father, this clue might lead you to think that the bookbinder must be a woman. However, the father may have adopted the son and so the two may have different last names.

Solution:

(Before reading this solution, see if you can solve the problem yourself.)

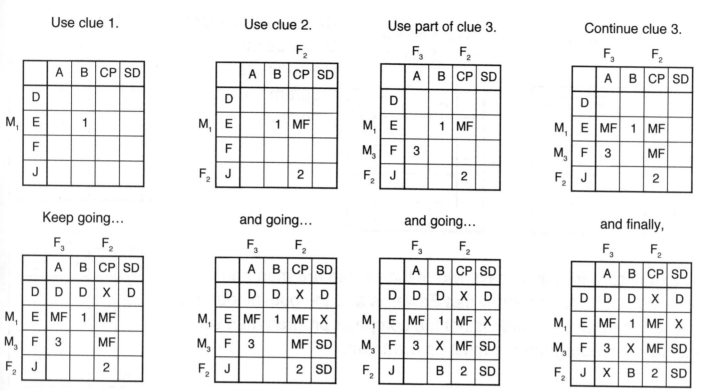

So the solution to the problem is this: Davis, computer programmer, female; Edwards, skin diver, male; Farman, bookbinder, male; Jones, astronaut, female.

Sometimes a problem will include a clue in the general information instead of in a numbered item.

EXAMPLE 4

Problem: Two men and two women (Davis, Edwards, Farman, and Jones) are an astronaut, a bookbinder, a computer programmer, and a skin diver. Find each person's job and sex.

1. Edwards is the bookbinder's son.

2. The bookbinder is the computer programmer's son.

3. Farman is not a woman.

4. Jones and the skin diver are married.

5. Davis is not the astronaut.

Solution:

(Try to do this one yourself before reading the solution.)

Use clue 1.

	A	B	CP	SD
D				
M₁ E		1		
F				
J				

Use the obvious part of clue 2.

M₂

	A	B	CP	SD
D				
M₁ E		1		
F				
J				

By combining clues 1 and 2, we see that Edwards must be the computer programmer's grandson.

M₂

	A	B	CP	SD
D				
M₁ E		1	1,2	
F				
J				

The general information says two of the people are men and two are women. So far we know that Edwards and the bookbinder are the two men. But Edwards is not the computer programmer, so the computer programmer must be a woman.

M₂ F₂

	A	B	CP	SD
D				
M₁ E		1	1,2	
F				
J				

Use *clue 3*. Since Farman is not a woman, Farman is a man.

M₂ F₂

	A	B	CP	SD
D				
M₁ E		1	1,2	
M₃ F			MF	
J				

But now both Edwards and Farman are men, so Davis and Jones are women.

M₂ F₂

	A	B	CP	SD
F₃ D		FM		
M₁ E		1	1,2	
M₃ F			MF	
F₃ J		FM		

We now X the only blank left in the "B" column. This matches up in the "F" row, so we fill in the rest of the "F" row.

M₂ F₂

	A	B	CP	SD
F₃ D		FM		
M₁ E		1	1,2	
M₃ F	F	X	MF	F
F₃ J		FM		

Use *clue 4.* Since Jones is female, the skin diver must be male.

Clue 4, step 1

	A	B	CP	SD
		M_2	F_2	M_4
F_3 D		FM		
M_1 E		1	1,2	
M_3 F	F	X	MF	F
F_3 J		FM		

Clue 4, step 2

	A	B	CP	SD
		M_2	F_2	M_4
F_3 D		FM		FM
M_1 E		1	1,2	
M_3 F	F	X	MF	F
F_3 J		FM		FM

Since only two of the jobs are held by men, the astronaut must be a woman.

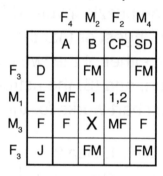

Clue 4, step 3

	A	B	CP	SD
	F_4	M_2	F_2	M_4
F_3 D		FM		FM
M_1 E		1	1,2	
M_3 F	F	X	MF	F
F_3 J		FM		FM

Clue 4, step 4

	A	B	CP	SD
	F_4	M_2	F_2	M_4
F_3 D		FM		FM
M_1 E	MF	1	1,2	
M_3 F	F	X	MF	F
F_3 J		FM		FM

Clue 4, step 5

	A	B	CP	SD
	F_4	M_2	F_2	M_4
F_3 D		FM		FM
M_1 E	MF	1	1,2	X
M_3 F	F	X	MF	F
F_3 J		FM		FM

Now we use *clue 5.*

Clue 5, step 1

	A	B	CP	SD
	F_4	M_2	F_2	M_4
F_3 D	5	FM		FM
M_1 E	MF	1	1,2	X
M_3 F	F	X	MF	F
F_3 J		FM		FM

Clue 5, step 2

	A	B	CP	SD
	F_4	M_2	F_2	M_4
F_3 D	5	FM	X	FM
M_1 E	MF	1	1,2	X
M_3 F	F	X	MF	F
F_3 J		FM		FM

Clue 5, step 3

	A	B	CP	SD
	F_4	M_2	F_2	M_4
F_3 D	5	FM	X	FM
M_1 E	MF	1	1,2	X
M_3 F	F	X	MF	F
F_3 J		FM	CP	FM

Clue 5, step 4

	A	B	CP	SD
	F_4	M_2	F_2	M_4
F_3 D	5	FM	X	FM
M_1 E	MF	1	1,2	X
M_3 F	F	X	MF	F
F_3 J	X	FM	CP	FM

Our solution is the same as for the previous problem: Davis, computer programmer, female; Edwards, skin diver, male; Farman, bookbinder, male; Jones, astronaut, female.

THREE-DIMENSIONAL PROBLEMS

To solve a three-dimensional problem, we make the chart so that each item in each list can be compared with each item in both other lists.

EXAMPLE 1

Problem: Davis, Edwards, and Farman are an astronaut, a bookbinder, and a skin diver. Their ages are 25, 30, and 35. Match each person's name, job, and age.

1. Davis is younger than the astronaut but older than Farman.

2. The skin diver is younger than the bookbinder.

Solution: To help keep our thinking straight on clue 1, we'll write in mathematical symbols: F < D < A. Then Farman is the youngest, Davis is in the middle, and the astronaut is the oldest. So Farman is 25, Davis is 30, and the astronaut is 35.

It is important to notice here that if the puzzle involved four people instead of three, we could not say that Farman is the youngest or that the astronaut is the oldest. The most we could say is (1) Farman is not either of the two oldest people, (2) Davis is not either the oldest or the youngest person, and (3) the astronaut is not either of the two youngest people. Let's look at how the chart works for this kind of problem.

Clue 1, step 1

	A	B	SD	25	30	35
D	1				X	
E						
F	1			X		
25						
30						
35	X					

Clue 1, step 2

	A	B	SD	25	30	35
D	1			25	X	D
E				25	30	
F	1			X	F	F
25	A					
30	A					
35	X	35	35			

Clue 1, step 3

	A	B	SD	25	30	35
D	1			25	X	D
E	X	E	E	25	30	X
F	1			X	F	F
25	A					
30	A					
35	X	35	35			

Clue 2 says the skin diver is younger than the bookbinder. The chart (from *clue 1, step 3*) says that Edwards, the astronaut, is 35. This leaves ages 25 and 30. So the skin diver is 25 and the bookbinder is 30. But we know from the chart that Farman is 25 and Davis is 30. So Farman is the skin diver and Davis is the bookbinder.

Solution: Davis, bookbinder, 30; Edwards, astronaut, 35; Farman, skin diver, 25.

	A	B	SD	25	30	35
D	1	X	SD	25	X	D
E	X	E	E	25	30	X
F	1	F	X	X	F	F
25	A	25	X			
30	A	X	SD			
35	X	35	35			

EXAMPLE 2

Problem: Davis, Edwards, Farman, and Gurley are an astronaut, a bookbinder, a plumber, and a skin diver. Their first names are Harold, Jenny, Ken, and Laura. Match up each person's full name and job.

1. Farman and the astronaut joined the same fraternity in college.

2. Edwards said she'd teach Jenny how to swim.

3. Ken asked the plumber if he could install a solar heating system for him.

4. Davis enjoys her work.

Solution: (Can you solve this one before reading the solution below?)

Clue 1
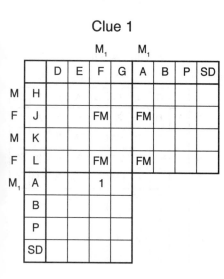

Clue 2
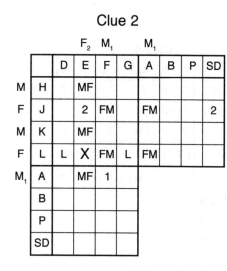

Clue 3, step 1
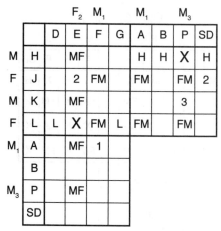

Clue 3, step 2
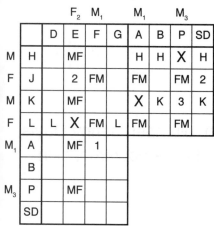

Clue 3, step 3*

*The "F" column says Farman is not the astronaut (*clue 1*). But step 2 of *clue 3* says Ken is the astronaut. Therefore, Ken is not Farman.

Clue 3, step 4

		D	E F_2	F M_1	G	A M_1	B	P M_3	SD
M	H		MF			H	H	X	H
F	J		2	FM		FM	X	FM	2
M	K		MF	3,1		X	K	3	K
F	L	L	X	FM	L	FM	B	FM	X
M_1	A		MF	1					
	B								
M_3	P		MF						
	SD								

Clue 3, step 5

		D	E F_2	F M_1	G	A M_1	B	P M_3	SD
M	H	H	MF	X	H	H	H	X	H
F	J		2	FM		FM	X	FM	2
M	K		MF	3,1		X	K	3	K
F	L	L	X	FM	L	FM	B	FM	X
M_1	A		MF	1					
	B								
M_3	P		MF						
	SD								

Clue 3, step 6

		D	E F_2	F M_1	G	A M_1	B	P M_3	SD
M	H	H	MF	X	H	H	H	X	H
F	J		2	FM		FM	X	FM	2
M	K		MF	3,1		X	K	3	K
F	L	L	X	FM	L	FM	B	FM	X
M_1	A		MF	1					
	B			F					
M_3	P	P	MF	X	P				
	SD			F					

Clue 3, step 7

		D	E F_2	F M_1	G	A M_1	B	P M_3	SD
M	H	H	MF	X	H	H	H	X	H
F	J		2	FM		FM	X	FM	2
M	K		MF	3,1		X	K	3	K
F	L	L	X	FM	L	FM	B	FM	X
M_1	A		MF	1					
	B		E	F					
M_3	P	P	MF	X	P				
	SD	SD	X	F	SD				

Clue 4, step 1

		D F_4	E F_2	F M_1	G	A M_1	B	P M_3	SD
M	H	H	MF	X	H	H	H	X	H
F	J	X	2	FM	J	FM	X	FM	2
M	K	MF	MF	3,1		X	K	3	K
F	L	L	X	FM	L	FM	B	FM	X
M_1	A		MF	1					
	B		E	F					
M_3	P	P	MF	X	P				
	SD	SD	X	F	SD				

Clue 4, step 2

		D F_4	E F_2	F M_1	G	A M_1	B	P M_3	SD
M	H	H	MF	X	H	H	H	X	H
F	J	X	2	FM	J	FM	X	FM	2
M	K	MF	MF	3,1		X	K	3	K
F	L	L	X	FM	L	FM	B	FM	X
M_1	A	D	MF	1					
	B	X	E	F	B				
M_3	P	P	MF	X	P				
	SD	SD	X	F	SD				

Clue 4, step 3

		D F_4	E F_2	F M_1	G	A M_1	B	P M_3	SD
M	H	H	MF	X	H	H	H	X	H
F	J	X	2	FM	J	FM	X	FM	2
M	K	MF	MF	3,1	X	X	K	3	K
F	L	L	X	FM	L	FM	B	FM	X
M_1	A	D	MF	1	X				
	B	X	E	F	B				
M_3	P	P	MF	X	P				
	SD	SD	X	F	SD				

The solution is this: Harold Farman, plumber; Jenny Davis, bookbinder; Ken Gurley, astronaut; Laura Edwards, skin diver

3 1170 00682 4118